My
Special Unicorn

An enchanted fill-in journal

Do you love unicorns and all things magical? Then this adorable journal is the perfect place to share your a-neigh-zing adventures! You can treasure this journal forever, and look back on all the magical moments you had this year.

Inside you'll find space to write down all about who you are and the exciting things you got up to each month. There's also lots of awesome activities, fun fill-ins and cute quizzes for you to try out on your own or with friends and family.

Turn the page to begin!

All About You!

It's time to discover the magic in you! Use these pages to fill in all about you and your life.

My name is

My nickname is

I am ____ years old.

My birthday is on

My hair is

My eyes are

My favourite colour is

My favourite food is

List three things that are a-neigh-zing about you:

Draw a picture or stick a photo of you here.

All About Your Life

Home is where the heart is! Use these pages
to write all about your home and family.

Draw a picture or stick a photo of where you live.

I have lived here for .... years.

My favourite thing about where I live is:

....

....

....

Describe your family:

....

....

....

....

Draw a picture or stick a photo of your family here.

Your Time to Shine

Dreaming big is amazing, but little dreams are at the heart of every great achievement. Turn your year into twelve mini adventures by setting yourself a goal for each month.

January

February

March

April

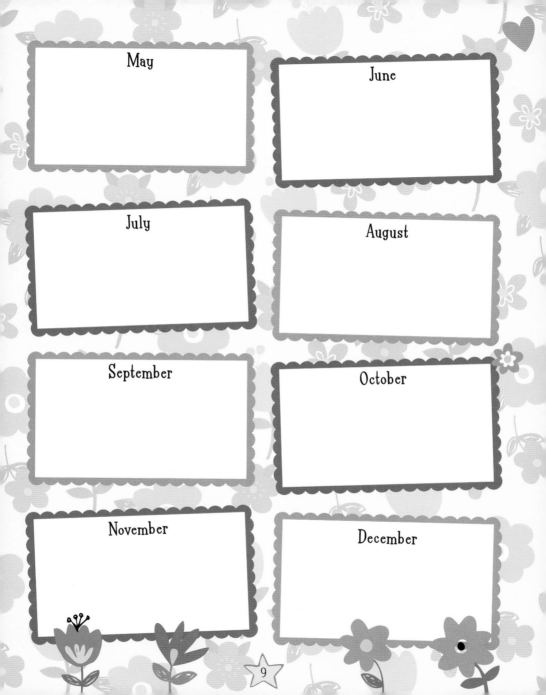

May

June

July

August

September

October

November

December

Discover Your Fortune

Do you have a question about the future that you really want to know the answer to? Wonder no more! Create this magical fortune-teller to reveal all.

How to make:

1. Ask an adult to help you cut out the fortune-teller, then place the decorated side face up.

2. Fold each corner into the centre to make a diamond shape.

3. Flip it over, and fold the new corners into the middle again.

4. Fold the square in half.

5. Put your thumbs and forefingers under each flap, and then push the four corners together then apart to make your fortune-teller open and close.

Share with your friends, and record your results here:

Name:

Fortune:

Name:

Fortune:

Name:

Fortune:

How to play

1. Ask the fortune-teller a "yes" or "no" question about your future.
2. Choose a colour and spell the name out loud, opening and closing the fortune-teller for each letter, G-R-E-E-N would mean you open and close your fortune teller five times.
3. Then pick a number and open and close the fortune-teller that number of times.
4. Now choose another number to reveal your answer. (Remember: nothing is set in stone and you hold the key to your destiny.)

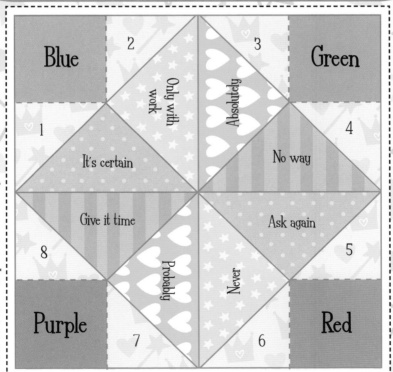

Blue

2

3

Green

Only with work

Absolutely

1

It's certain

No way

4

Give it time

Ask again

8

5

Probably

Never

Purple

7

6

Red

Ask an adult to help with the cutting.

Unicorn Wonders

Every unicorn is special, and has lots
of qualities that make them unique –
just like you! Write all about your unicorn,
and discover the magical world of
these cute creatures.

All About Your Unicorn

Bring your magical unicorn to life by using
the prompts below to help you design
and create your own special friend.

Name: ....

Age: ....

Horn colour: ....

Mane colour: ....

Coat colour: ....

Favourite hangout: ....

Mystical powers: ....

....

....

Now draw a picture of your magical unicorn.

Cute Companion

Every unicorn has their own unique personality. Take this quiz to find out what your ideal companion would be like.

1. Which of these words best describes you?
    a) Fun
    b) Caring
    c) Brave
    d) Creative

2. What is your favourite season?
a) Spring - you're always out and about,
enjoying the perfect weather

b) Autumn - you love the beautiful colours
and crisp evening chill

c) Winter - you like to wrap up warm and
spend time with your family

d) Summer - you're all about having fun in the sun
and hanging out with friends

3. What is your favourite colour?

a)   b)   c)   d)

4. What is your best skill?

a) Fashion, hair and make-up

b) Reading and learning new things

c) Telling jokes and making people laugh

d) Drawing, painting or baking - anything creative!

5. What is your favourite thing to do with your friends?

a) Shop 'til you drop - trying on different outfits and stylish selfies

b) Relaxing - picnics in the park or just chatting the day away

c) Out and about - awesome adventures or planning the next party

d) Create and discover - baking treats and discovering new places

6) What would you like to be when you're older?

a) A singer or dancer

b) A teacher or doctor

c) An athlete or explorer

d) An artist or inventor

Turn the page to discover your perfect pal!

Mostly 'a's - Social Star

Your companion is the life and soul of her blessing (that's the special term for a group of unicorns!). Her personality shines brightly, but she'll never let it overshadow her friends.

Your uni-qualities: friendly, confident, enthusiastic

Mostly 'b's - Heartwarming Hero

Your ideal unicorn companion is kind and gentle. You can usually find her helping out and taking care of her neigh-bours. Though she is sometimes shy, she will always stand up for her friends when they need her.

Your uni-qualities: supportive, calm, loyal

Mostly 'c's - Active Adventurer

Ready, set, gallop! Your perfect unicorn companion is a real thrill seeker, just like you! Your unique unicorn is always on her hooves, but she's never too busy to make time for her friends.

Your uni-qualities: lively, energetic, brave

Mostly 'd's - Creative Creature

Your unicorn has her own unique style, so she's the perfect match for your creative personality. From the latest forest fashions to moonlit musicals, your special friend is always discovering new things.

Your uni-qualities:

imaginative, artistic, dreamy

Get your friends to take the quiz, and record their magical matches.

19

Best Blessing

You and your friends each have a secret unicorn identity that's just waiting to be discovered. Follow the steps below to reveal the unique unicorn in you.

Your unicorn name

Pick the letter that your first name begins with:

a: Apple
b: Butterfly
c: Cinnamon
d: Dazzling
e: Emerald
f: Flutter
g: Glitter

h: Harmony
i: Iridescent
j: Jewel
k: Kisses
l: Lightning
m: Meadow
n: Nettle

o: Ocean
p: Phoenix
q: Queen
r: Rose
s: Sunshine
t: Twilight
u: Unity

v: Venus
w: Waterfall
x: Xena
y: Young
z: Zodiac

Pick the month you are born in:

January: Newmoon
February: Shimmermist
March: Rainbowshine
April: Twinkleshy

May: Stardust
June: Ivyqueen
July: Fireglow
August: Goldenhorn

September: Nightglimmer
October: Flowerbloom
November: Moonbeam
December: Shadowplay

Your unicorn look

You were born on:

Monday
Tuesday
Wednesday
Thursday
Friday
Saturday
Sunday

Your horn colour is:

Silver
Pink
Purple
Multicoloured
Gold
Blue
Bronze

Your hair colour is:

Brown
Blonde
Red
Black

Your mane colour is:

Purple
Pink
Blue
Multicoloured

Your unicorn hangout

Your eye colour is:

Brown
Blue
Green

Enchanted forest
Magical lagoon
Anywhere and everywhere!

Write down your results here:

My unicorn name: ....

My unicorn look: a .... horn and a .... mane

My unicorn hangout: ....

Using the same method, work out what all your friends' unicorns would be called. Write them down here so you don't forget!

Name: .... My unicorn name: ....

My unicorn look: a .... horn and a .... mane

My unicorn hangout: ....

Name: .... My unicorn name: ....

My unicorn look: a .... horn and a .... mane

My unicorn hangout: ....

Name: .... My unicorn name: ....

My unicorn look: a .... horn and a .... mane

My unicorn hangout: ....

Name: .... My unicorn name: ....

My unicorn look: a .... horn and a .... mane

My unicorn hangout: ....

Name: .... My unicorn name: ....

My unicorn look: a .... horn and a .... mane

My unicorn hangout: ....

Name: .... My unicorn name: ....

My unicorn look: a .... horn and a .... mane

My unicorn hangout: ....

Friends Forever

You and your friends will each have your own adventures, but the memories you share will always be carried in your heart. Make sure you never forget them by recording your journey together.

Friendship File

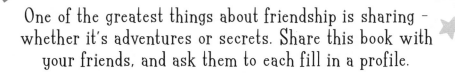

One of the greatest things about friendship is sharing — whether it's adventures or secrets. Share this book with your friends, and ask them to each fill in a profile.

Name: ....

Nickname: ....

Age: ....

Favourite colour: ....

Your unicorn's name: ....

List three things that are a-neigh-zing about you:

....

Name: ....

Nickname: ....

Age: ....

Favourite colour: ....

Your unicorn's name: ....

List three things that are a-neigh-zing about you:

....

Name: ....

Nickname: ....

Age: ....

Favourite colour: ....

Your unicorn's name: ....

List three things that are a-neigh-zing about you:

....

Name: ....

Nickname: ....

Age: ....

Favourite colour: ....

Your unicorn's name: ....

List three things that are a-neigh-zing about you:

....

Name: ....

Nickname: ....

Age: ....

Favourite colour: ....

Your unicorn's name: ....

List three things that are a-neigh-zing about you:

....

Our Friendship Story

All friendships have a great story to go with them.
Celebrate the brave beginning of your journey together.

How did you all meet? ....

What did you think of everyone at first? ....

....

Choose a name for your friendship group: ....

Tick the things you like to do together:

Go shopping	Sing
Laugh	Watch TV or films
Bake	Have parties
Sports	Dance
Play outside	Share secrets
Give each other makeovers	Listen to music
Chat	

Make your very own friendship gallery by sticking your favourite pictures of you and your friends here.

Special Friends

Whether you're soulmate sisters or different divas,
you can find your friendship score using this calculation.

1. First, write "**THE MAGIC OF FRIENDSHIP**" on a piece of paper.

2. Then write your name underneath, and count how many times each letter of your name appears in "**THE MAGIC OF FRIENDSHIP**". Make sure you record the number under each letter.

3. Add up the numbers underneath your name. If you get a double figure, add those two numbers together so you're left with a single number (for example, 15 would become 6).

4. Now choose a friend, and repeat these steps with their name.

5. To find your friendship score, put the two numbers next to each other - so if your number is 4 and your friend's is 7, you have a friendship score of 47%.

Here's an example to help you:

THE MAGIC OF FRIENDSHIP

AARABI   CHARLIE

111102 = 9   121132 = 10 =1+ 0 = 1

Friendship score: 91%

Your score...

Friendship score: 0-25%

You still have lots to learn about each other, but you can become better friends by spending more quality time together.

Friendship score: 26-50%

You're already good friends, but you don't always agree on everything. It's great to be different, just make sure you always listen to each other.

Friendship score: 51-75%

You and your pal love to share - whether it's jokes or secrets. Even though you know each other so well already, there's still lots more to discover.

Friendship score: 76-100%

You two were meant to be, and a friendship like yours is truly special! You know you can always rely on each other.

Magical Memories

The moments you share with your friends stay with you forever. Write down some of your favourite memories from the time you've spent together.

What's the funniest thing that's ever happened to you and your friends?

....

What's the nicest thing a friend has ever done for you?

....

Which memory makes you smile inside and out?

....

Do you have any embarrassing friendship memories?

....

Have you and your friends ever got into trouble?

....

Ask your friends and family about their favourite memory of you,
and write down what they say.

This is ....'s favourite memory of me:

This is ....'s favourite memory of me:

This is ....'s favourite memory of me:

This is ....'s favourite memory of me:

A-neigh-zing Activities

Feel inspired by these cute crafts and amazing activities. You can share your creations with your friends.

Make sure you ask an adult to help you with all these activities!

Super Sleepover

Sleepovers are such a great way to have fun with your friends. Try out some of the tips below to help make your sleepover exta-special.

* **Ask an adult**: it's important to make sure you ask permission to host your sleepover. You'll also need help with the recipes and activities in this book.

* **Be prepared**: if you're planning to make some of the recipes or other activities in this book then make sure you have all your ingredients ready ahead of time!

* **Get comfy**: ask your friends to bring some cosy jammies so you can all chill out in style.

* **Ask the team**: if you want to watch a film or play a game with your friends, take a vote to make sure everyone is happy.

* **Ask for extras**: ask your friends to bring some of their own nail varnishes or make-up with them. That way you'll have loads to choose from!

* **Ditch the tech**: as tempting as it is to play on your phones, tablets or computers, try to take this time to turn off your tech and spend some quality offline time with your friends.

Ask an adult to help you with these fun activities.

Pin the horn on the unicorn

You will need:

* a printout of a unicorn
* a cut-out unicorn horn (for each player)
* sticky tack or sticky tape

How to play:

1. Pin up your unicorn picture, and write the name of each participant on a horn.
2. Blindfold each person and spin them three times. Point them forwards towards the poster, but a metre or two back. The goal is for them to walk forwards and to stick the horn on the unicorn.
3. Players cannot touch the board to see the other pieces.
4. The closest horn to the actual unicorn horn wins a prize.

Make a magical den

You will need:

* space for your den
* pillows and blankets
* chairs or other items to prop things up on
* battery-operated fairy lights (optional)

How to play:

1. Careful! Make sure you ask an adult first before moving furniture and other items around.
2. Gather all the pillows and blankets you can find and drape them all over chairs, a clothes airer or something similar to make a comfortable, hidden den.
3. If you have fairy lights, drape them inside using tape or tie them up. Then get cosy inside your den with your friends for giggles and gossip.

Sweet Dreams

In the morning, write all about the magical dreams you and your friends had while you were sleeping.

Last night .... dreamed that...

Last night .... dreamed that...

Last night .... dreamed that...

Last night .... dreamed that...

Sleeping Secrets

Have you ever wondered what your dreams mean?
Read on to discover what your dreams say about you...

Water

Water in dreams can represent your emotions, so the type of water is important! A waterfall might mean that you should go with the flow, and a stormy sea could show that you're feeling a bit unsettled.

Flying

If you were dreaming of soaring high in the sky, then you must be flying high on life. Whether you achieved a goal or aced a test in school, you're feeling empowered and floating on cloud nine.

A bridge

Dreaming of a bridge could show that you're about to enter a new chapter in your life. Maybe something big at school or home is going to change, or perhaps you're about to go on an exciting adventure.

Being chased

If you're being chased in your dream, it might mean that you're running away from something or someone in real life. Is there anything you're worried about? Talking to a friend or a teacher will help you feel less anxious.

Magical Manicures

Give you and your friends a marvellous manicure.
Follow the steps below to create beautiful rainbow hands.

You will need:

* a nail file
* five different-coloured nail varnishes (if you have them, red, orange, yellow, green and a blue or purple would be best, to match the colours of the rainbow)
* clear gitter nail varnish (which you can see through)
* a topcoat (optional)

How to:

1. File your nails into a neat shape. Remember, it's best to always file in the same direction, rather than going from side to side.

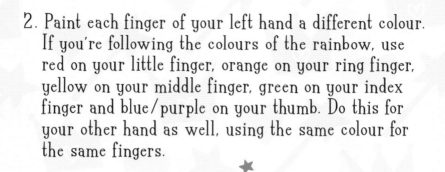

2. Paint each finger of your left hand a different colour. If you're following the colours of the rainbow, use red on your little finger, orange on your ring finger, yellow on your middle finger, green on your index finger and blue/purple on your thumb. Do this for your other hand as well, using the same colour for the same fingers.

3. Apply two coats of polish on to each finger and wait for them to dry.

4. Add a layer of glitter nail polish to each of your fingers and wait for it to dry.

5. If you have a topcoat, apply it now. This will help your nail polish stay in place.

6. You're done! Now you should have shiny, sparkly, rainbow hands!

When using nail varnish, be careful not to spill it!

Unicorn Tail Friendship Bracelets

The magic of friendship ties everyone together!
Make these special friendship bracelets with
your friends at your next sleepover.

You will need:

* coloured ribbons
* scissors
* sticky tape

How to:

1. Choose ribbon in three colours that you think represent your friend.

2. Cut the three ribbons into equal lengths. You'll need at least enough to go round your wrist three times, but cut extra if you're not sure.

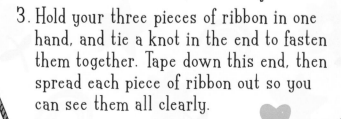

3. Hold your three pieces of ribbon in one hand, and tie a knot in the end to fasten them together. Tape down this end, then spread each piece of ribbon out so you can see them all clearly.

4. Start with the piece on the left, and take it over the piece in the middle. Lay it down there, so that it becomes the middle piece.

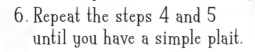

5. Now lift the piece on the right, and take that over so that it becomes the middle piece.

6. Repeat the steps 4 and 5 until you have a simple plait.

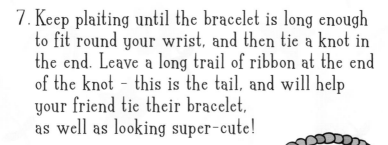

7. Keep plaiting until the bracelet is long enough to fit round your wrist, and then tie a knot in the end. Leave a long trail of ribbon at the end of the knot - this is the tail, and will help your friend tie their bracelet, as well as looking super-cute!

8. You're finished! Now help your friend make a matching one for you.

Unicorn Treats

Spread the love with these unicorn-themed
recipes, and create some mouth-watering morsels
to share with your friends and family.

Make sure
you ask an
adult to help you
with all these
recipes!

Rainbow Cookies

Bake these beautiful biscuits for your friends and family –
they're as yummy as they are colourful!

You will need:

* 225 g butter

* 100 g caster sugar

* 200 g brown sugar

* 1 teaspoon vanilla extract

* 2 eggs

* 350 g Smarties (or any other brightly-
  coloured chocolate)

* 350 g plain flour

* 1 teaspoon bicarbonate of soda

* 1 teaspoon of salt

This recipe makes
enough for approximately
12 to 15 cookies,
depending on how big
they are.

How to make them:

1. Ask an adult to preheat your oven to 190°C/375°F/ gas mark 5.

2. In a large bowl, combine the butter, caster sugar, brown sugar and vanilla extract. Stir until this is light and fluffy, then beat in the eggs.

3. Weigh out your flour into a medium-sized bowl and combine it with the bicarbonate of soda and salt. Then fold it into your sugar and butter mixture. Finally, add in your coloured-chocolate and stir. You've now made your cookie dough!

4. Start taking small amounts of dough and rolling it into balls. Place the balls on two baking trays with lots of space between them. Bake them for 10-12 minutes, depending on how gooey you like them.

5. Leave them to cool on the baking trays (or on a wire rack), then share with friends. Delicious!

Ask an adult to help you!

Unicorn Hot Chocolate

Snuggle up with a mug of this magical hot chocolate.

You will need:

* 300 ml of milk
* 50 g of chopped white chocolate
* pink food colouring

To Serve:

* 100 ml of double or single cream
* marshmallows (optional)
* sprinkles (optional)

How to make it:

1. Whip up the double/single cream (if using) until it just holds its shape.

2. Pour the milk into a small pan and heat until simmering, stirring to stop it scorching.

3. Take the pan off the heat and add the white chocolate then stir until the chocolate has fully melted.

4. Add food colouring to turn the mixture pastel pink.

5. When the mixture is hot enough, pour into cups. You could add marshmallows, sprinkles and/or whipped cream for an extra treat, or simply serve as is.

Glittering Goodness

Ask an adult to help you!

Make this delicious smoothie in the morning
to help you gallop into the day.

You will need:

* 300 g of strawberries (fresh or frozen)
* 500 ml of Greek yogurt
* 3/4 tbsp of honey
* a large handful of ice
* edible glitter (optional)

How to make it:

1. If you are using fresh berries, make sure they're clean and any stalks have been removed. Then slice into small pieces (you don't have to worry about this if the berries are frozen).

2. Ask an adult to help you put the berries, yogurt, honey and ice into a blender and blend until smooth. If your blender doesn't take ice, simply add the ice in at the end instead.

3. Pour into glasses and serve. For that extra special touch, sprinke with edible glitter.

Ask an adult to help you!

Magical Mug Cake

This rainbow mug cake is as easy as it is delicious. This is the perfect amount for one mug, but if you want to make more just repeat the recipe.

You will need:

For the cake:

* 4 tablespoons flour
* 1/2 teaspoon baking powder
* 3 tablespoons sugar
* 1/2 tablespoon butter, softened (and a little bit extra for greasing)
* 4 tablespoons milk
* 1/2 teaspoon vanilla extract
* 1 pinch of salt
* 1 teaspoon coloured sprinkles

For the icing:

* 8 tablespoons icing sugar
* 2 tablespoons unsalted butter (at room temperature)
* 1/4 teaspoon vanilla extract
* coloured sprinkles (optional)

How to make it:

1. Mix all of the cake ingredients in a bowl until the mixture is creamy and smooth.

2. Pour the mixed ingredients into a decent sized mug. Greasing the mug with a little bit of butter first will help to stop it sticking.

3. Ask an adult to help you microwave your mug for 90 seconds.

4. Ask an adult to take your mug out of the microwave and leave it to cool.

5. Mix together the icing ingredients in a bowl until you have smooth, shiny icing.

6. Spread your icing either onto your cake in the mug or pop the cake out of the mug on to a plate and then ice it.

7. Cover with sprinkles and enjoy!

Cute Culture

All the little things you like add
up to create your unique style and
personality. Write down all about
your favourite films and books, and
make new discoveries along the way.

Live, Laugh, Learn

Friends and fun are important, but there's also lots of
magical things to discover at school. Fill in all about
your top teachers and special subjects.

My favourite subject is:

....

I like this subject because:

....

My favourite teacher is:

....

I like this teacher because:

....

When I'm older, I want to be:

....

Unicorn Uniform

Design a magical new outfit for you to wear at school.

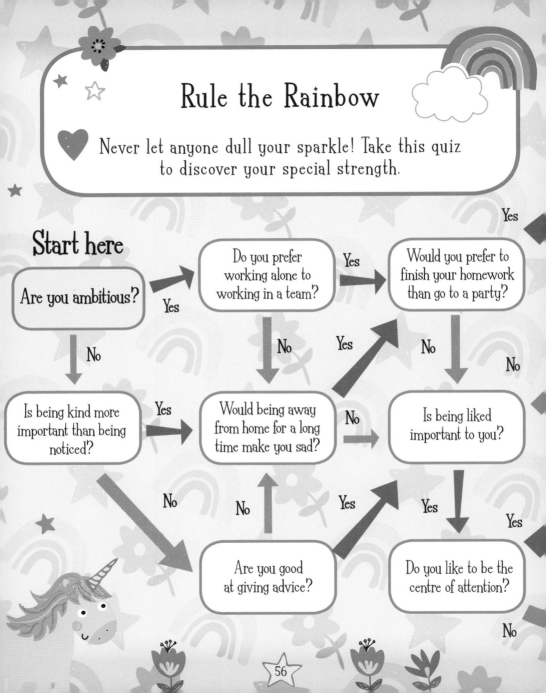

Rule the Rainbow

Never let anyone dull your sparkle! Take this quiz to discover your special strength.

Start here

Are you ambitious?

→ Yes → Do you prefer working alone to working in a team?

→ Yes → Would you prefer to finish your homework than go to a party?

Yes

No

No

Yes

No

No

Is being kind more important than being noticed?

→ Yes → Would being away from home for a long time make you sad?

→ No → Is being liked important to you?

No

No

Yes

Yes

Yes

Are you good at giving advice?

Do you like to be the centre of attention?

Yes

No

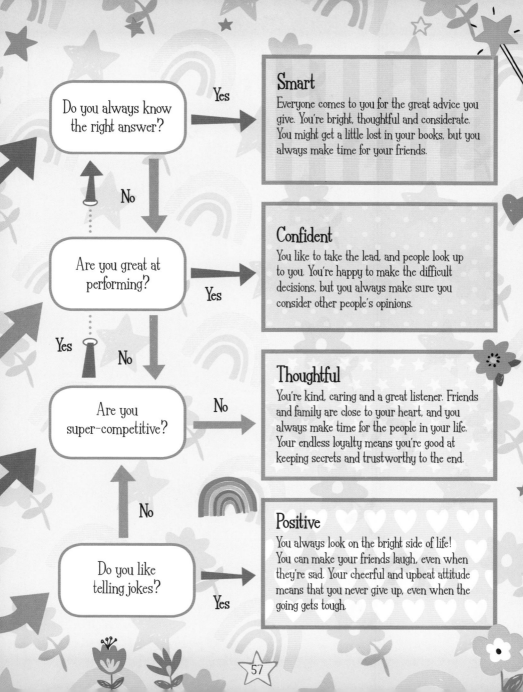

Do you always know the right answer?

Yes →

Smart
Everyone comes to you for the great advice you give. You're bright, thoughtful and considerate. You might get a little lost in your books, but you always make time for your friends.

No

Are you great at performing?

Yes →

Confident
You like to take the lead, and people look up to you. You're happy to make the difficult decisions, but you always make sure you consider other people's opinions.

Yes

No

Are you super-competitive?

No →

Thoughtful
You're kind, caring and a great listener. Friends and family are close to your heart, and you always make time for the people in your life. Your endless loyalty means you're good at keeping secrets and trustworthy to the end.

No

Do you like telling jokes?

Yes →

Positive
You always look on the bright side of life! You can make your friends laugh, even when they're sad. Your cheerful and upbeat attitude means that you never give up, even when the going gets tough.

Movie Magic

Lights, camera, action! Your favourite TV shows and films can take you on exciting adventures from the comfort of your own home. Fill in all about your favourite flicks.

Favourite film or TV series: ....

Why: ....

....

Favourite female actor: ....

Why: ....

....

Favourite male actor: ....

Why: ....

....

Film or TV show recommendations I've been given: ....

....

Design a new poster for your favourite film
or a movie you'd like to make yourself.

Beautiful Books

The power of words can take you on a mystical journey.
Fill in all about the books you've read recently.

Favourite book: ....

Why: ....

....

Favourite author: ....

Why: ....

....

Books I want to read next: ....

....

Book recommendations I've been given: ....

....

Wonderful Words

You're the star of your own story! Create your own exciting tale and see where your imagination takes you.

The Start

Answer these questions to set the scene.

Will your story have magic in it?

Yes   No

Where is your story set?

An enchanted castle   A mystical mountain

An underwater kingdom   A magical forest

An idea of your own:

....

Will there be a villain to defeat?

Yes   No

Who are your characters?

Unicorns	Witches
Monsters	Humans

An idea of your own:

....

Will everyone live happily ever after?

Yes	No

What happens in your story?

A hidden world is discovered	A secret is revealed
An important object is stolen	A mysterious stranger arrives

An idea of your own:

....

Write down your story here! If you run out of space,
continue on a separate piece of paper and then stick it in.

Title of your story:

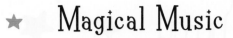

Magical Music

Do you like to sing your heart out? Or do you prefer to chill to some tunes? Fill in all about your best beats here.

Favourite artist/band:..

Why:...

....

Favourite song:...

Why:...

....

Bands I want to see live:..

....

Artists/bands recommendations I've been given: ....

....

Dancing Spirit

It's time to put your best hoof forward!
Play this game with a friend and perform
your own special dances.

You will need:

* 1 dice
* a dance partner (optional)

1. Wave your hands

2. Spin

How to:

1. Take turns rolling the dice and write down the numbers that you roll.

2. Each number on the dice matches a dance move below. Make a list of the dance moves and then start dancing.

3. You can teach all your family and friends your a-neigh-zing moves.

5. Jump

3. Skip

4. Stamp your feet

6. Clap your hands

A-neigh-zing Adventures

Keeping special souvenirs, like photos and tickets, can help you remember the adventures you have with your friends. Stick some of your keepsakes below.

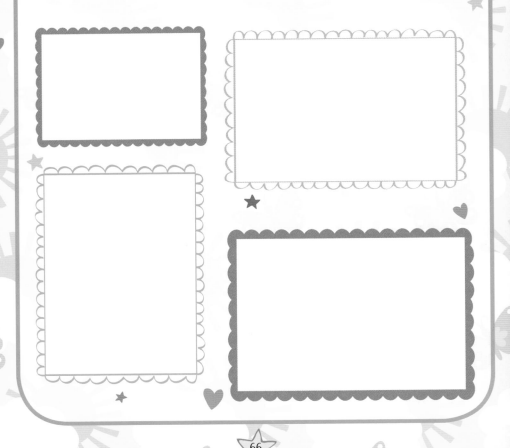

Dream up future travel plans for your own faraway fantasy.

If you could go anywhere in the world, where would you go?

....

Where would you stay?

....

Who would you go with?

....

What would you do? ....

....

....

....

....

Super Secret Journal

Write down all your a-neigh-zing
adventures and special secrets.
You can look back on the
magical memories you've had
from the past year.

January

Week 1

....

....

....

....

Week 2

....

....

....

....

Week 3

....

....

....

....

Week 4

....

....

....

....

February

Week 1

....

....

....

....

Week 2

....

....

....

....

Week 3

....

....

....

....

Week 4

....

....

....

....

March

Week 1

....

....

....

....

Week 2

....

....

....

....

Week 3

....

....

....

....

Week 4

....

....

....

....

April

Week 1

....
....
....
....

Week 2

....
....
....
....

Week 3

....

....

....

....

Week 4

....

....

....

....

May

Week 1

....

....

....

....

Week 2

....

....

....

....

Week 3

....

....

....

....

Week 4

....

....

....

....

June

Week 1

....

....

....

....

Week 2

....

....

....

....

Week 3

....

....

....

....

Week 4

....

....

....

....

July

Week 1

....

....

....

....

Week 2

....

....

....

....

Week 3

....

....

....

....

Week 4

....

....

....

....

August

Week 1

....

....

....

....

Week 2

....

....

....

....

Week 3

....

....

....

....

Week 4

....

....

....

....

September

Week 1

....

....

....

....

Week 2

....

....

....

....

Week 3

....

....

....

....

Week 4

....

....

....

....

October

Week 1

....

....

....

....

Week 2

....

....

....

....

Week 3

....

....

....

....

Week 4

....

....

....

....

89

November

Week 1

....

....

....

Week 2

....

....

....

Week 3

....

....

....

....

Week 4

....

....

....

....

December

Week 1

....

....

....

....

Week 2

....

....

....

....

Week 3

....

....

....

....

Week 4

....

....

....

....

Let Your Dreams Soar!

Where do you think you and your friends will be ten years from now? Write down your predictions here so you can see how many come true.

Me

I will live in: ....

With: ....

My job will be: ....

Because: ....

Name: ....

They will live in: ....

Their job will be: ....

Because: ....

Name: ....

They will live in: ....

Their job will be: ....

Because: ....